What Do We See?

A Division of The McGraw·Hill Companies

Columbus, Ohio

www.sra4kids.com

SRA/McGraw-Hill
A Division of The **McGraw·Hill** Companies

Send all inquiries to:
SRA/McGraw-Hill
8787 Orion Place
Columbus, OH 43240-4027

ISBN 0-07-569880-3
1 2 3 4 5 6 7 8 9 DBH 05 04 03 02 01

We are at the  . What do we see?

ZOO

3

We see a  .

giraffe

We see .

elephants

We see zebras .

6

We see .

monkeys

This is what we see at the !

ZOO